D1635478

Hello, fellow Bin Weevils! Tink and Clott here. Come and join us on a search-and-find adventure through the Binscape!

As you're about to discover, the Bin is the busiest it's ever been! We'll need your help searching the crowds for missing Bin Weevils, Bin Pets, and lost items and treasures. You'll find handy checklists on every page, plus a full page of even more things to search for at the back of the book.

You'll be amazed at what you might see in the busy scenes, so turn the page for some serious search-and-find fun!

First published 2012 by Macmillan Children's Books
a division of Macmillan Publishers Limited
20 New Wharf Road, London N1 9RR
Basingstoke and Oxford
Associated companies throughout the world
www.panmacmillan.com

ISBN 978-1-4472-0534-0

3 5 7 9 8 6 4 2

A CIP catalogue record for this book is available from the British Library.

Printed and bound in Europe

MENU

Wow, we've never seen Flum's Fountain so packed! Everybody's here to see Scribbles interview the elusive Nest Inspector. Ink was supposed to be taking notes, but he's nowhere to be seen. Or is he?
Can you spot:
Ink
Five Red Cowboy Hats
Seven lime-green Bin Weevils
Six Bin Pets

We've popped along to Dosh's Palace to see Dosh's balcony appearance. His sister, Posh, should be here somewhere, but we're having trouble spotting her in the crowds . . .
Can you spot:
Posh
Six Roman Helmets
Five Indian Chief Headdresses
Twenty Mulch notes

DOSH'S PALACE
20
500

Next stop: Tink's Tree. Tink is very proud of his tree – he insists on inspecting it every week to make sure things are running smoothly. Blimey, he's dashed off already!
Can you spot:
A red Bin Weevil attracting a lot of flies
Seven Elf Hats
Eight Witch's Hats
Five Policeman's Hats

Rock n Roll!
Let's Bowl!

The Rock 'n' Roll Party has finally hit the Binscape! We just need to find Slam so we can request a song on the jukebox!
Can you spot:
Eight electric guitars
Six purple Bin Weevils
Eight Super Spiky Hats
Slam
bowlin

A quick trip to the Bin Pet Shop has turned into chaos – Clott accidentally let all the pets out of their pen! We'd better give the Shop Owner a hand rounding them up. If we can find him, that is . . .
Can you spot:
The Shop Owner
Five red Bin Pets
Ten yellow Bin Pets
Ten juggling balls
Pet Mulch
gadgets and
Pet Mulch

Pet Mulch
PETS
&

Yikes! The Dragon has a severe case of hiccups. Gam has called for all members of the Secret Weevil Service to come to the Castle immediately to help get the situation under control.
Can you spot:
Gam
Six red Firefighter Helmets
Five orange-and-red Bin Pets
Five purple firefighters

We've managed to squeeze ourselves to the front of the crowds for the big race, so we've got a fantastic view of the action!
Can you spot:
A golden steering wheel
Eight oil cans
Five spanners
Six Rainbow Pixie Hats
DIRTVALLEY

Mmm, ice cream . . . it's the perfect snack for a hot day at the beach. Now then, we need to find Hem so that we can buy some stylish new Bucket Hats . . .
Can you spot:
Four blue buckets
Ten blue parasols
Eight strawberry ice creams
Hem selling Bucket Hats

CLUB FLING

It's party time ALL THE TIME at Club Fling, but we've never seen the place so packed! Can you help us find Fling and Zing? As you can see, we're in desperate need of some dance tips from the experts!
Can you spot:
Fling
Ten Traffic Cone Hats
Zing
Six Blue Striped Top Hats
DJ SLAM
POP HALL

Tum's
DINER
HE BEST
in Burger
his side
f the Bin!

We popped into Tum's Diner for a well-deserved snack, but we've been roped into serving customers whilst Tum and Slum take a break. They've asked us to bring them two Bin Burgers, but we can't see where they're sitting.
Can you spot:
Six slices of Chocolate Sludge Cake
Tum
Slum
Ten plates of Bin Bangers
MUD PIE

Aah, bliss. What better way to end a busy day than with a fun trip to the Slime Pool on Tycoon Island. It didn't take Clott long to get completely covered in slime!
Can you spot:
Five Bling Top Hats
Seven black-and-white Bin Weevils
Ten Checkered Top Hats
Six Peach on the Beach smoothies

SMOOTHIE
SHACK
WATER
SLIDE

KEEP ON SEARCHING!

The search-and-find fun doesn't stop here! These four characters are hiding in every scene in this book! Can you find them?

Tink Clott Kip Dr Weevil

Go back through the book and see if you can spot all these things. There's only one of each, and we're not telling you which scenes they're in!

We made a list of the top ten funniest things we saw on our adventure. Go back through the book and see if you can spot them all! You can get to know all these characters better on the Bin Weevils website.

- ☐ Dosh covered in slime from head to foot.
- ☐ Gong stubbing his toe.
- ☐ Gam showing off his dance moves.
- ☐ Scribbles having his picture taken with six Bin Pets.
- ☐ A green Bin Weevil buried in sand.
- ☐ Grunt on a pogo stick.
- ☐ A Bin Pet driving a racing car.
- ☐ Hem without a hat.
- ☐ Tab hiding from some confetti.
- ☐ Fling having a nap on a mushroom.

SCIENCE SECRET!

There are 25 test tubes of different colours hidden throughout this book. Can you find them all? Write down how many there are of each colour in the boxes here, and the numbers will form a secret code. Enter that code into the Mystery Code Machine at Lab's Lab to collect another exclusive nest item!

BACKWARDS BONUS!

Hold this page up to a mirror to reveal a secret code, then enter it into the Mystery Code Machine at Lab's Lab to unlock an exclusive nest item!

FAWZ75L9Z3P4